# Setpoint

## DIET

# Cookbook

**Lose Weight in 21 days and keep it off permanently.**

*By*

*Laura Williams*

**Disclaimer:**

The information provided in this book is designed to provide helpful information on the subjects discussed. The publisher and author are not responsible for any specific health or allergy needs that may require medical supervision and are not liable for any damages or negative consequences from any treatment, action, application or preparation, to any person reading or following the information in this book.

# Table of Contents

## The Setpoint Diet Cookbook: Secret to Weight Loss

You might be wondering if the setpoint diet is the secret to weight loss? Do you wish it is the answer you've been looking for, but doubt it will certainly bring you permanent weight loss results?

Every year approximately 45 million Americans attempt a new diet, and it's a good bet many of them try countless diets during the year. If you're one of the hundreds of millions of people out there frustrated by weight that keeps coming back, by failed promises from the weight loss industry and by the lack of progress you see each time you step on the scale, this cookbook can be of immense help.

The setpoint diet is a sure secret to permanent weight loss; and you won't have to count calories or be hungry — at all.

However, carrying extra weight here and there can be irritating. Your clothes may not fit perfectly. This extra weight may feel physically uncomfortable and also dangerous for your health. Weight loss limit the risk of most of these health issues, making permanent weight loss, if you lay blames on yourself for not succeeding on any of those diets you tried or if you feel guilt or shame. Note it that you have not failed those weight loss programs, they failed you. How could you possibly succeed when they gave you incorrect information to work with?

This cookbook is here to give you the correct information. Knowing the truth about how the metabolism works, information proven in thousands of research studies, you will finally know the secret to weight loss. You will finally succeed at losing weight and keeping it off permanently.

The body is more like the thermostat in your home. In this case, your internal thermostat "reads" the level of body fat you have. If you go under or over that amount of fat, your biological system takes action to bring your levels to what they should be.

Your body system like the digestive system, brain, and hormones talk to each other through a sophisticated communication feedback loop to synchronize the activities that keep your body at a specified level of fat. This is known as your setpoint weight, and your body tries its best to keep you within 10-15 pounds of this weight regardless of how much your slash calories or how hard you work out.

Nevertheless, if you significantly cut calories, the way you've been taught to do, you'll lose weight. However, your body fights back by slowing your metabolism, making you hungry, and triggering many other hormonal responses designed to hold onto the fat. The only way you can lose weight and keep it off permanently is to lower your setpoint weight. When you do that, your body will defend that lower weight, and you will lose weight with less effort.

The setpoint diet contains food groups scientifically proven to heal your trigger fat-burning hormones and lower your setpoint weight. It also recommends reducing or eliminating heavily processed foods, refined carbs, and foods with added sugar from your diet. It emphasizes whole foods as close to their natural states as possible.

## Your Delectable Setpoint Breakfast Recipes

Eggs Baked in Portobello Mushrooms

**Tip:**

This recipe is lovely for brunch, and substantial enough for a filling lunch or a meatless dinner.

**Prep Time 5 minutes**

**Cook Time 25 minutes**

**Total Time 30 minutes**

**Servings 2 servings**

**Ingredients**

Olive oil spray

½ teaspoon of black pepper (divided)

4 medium eggs

4 tablespoons of chopped parsley for garnish

4 large Portobello mushrooms (stem removed, wiped clean)

½ teaspoon of kosher salt (divided)

½ teaspoon of garlic powder

2 tablespoons of grated Parmesan cheese

**Directions:**

1. First, you heat broiler, setting temperature to high.

2. After which you set oven rack in the middle of the oven; line a baking sheet with foil.
3. After that, you spray the mushroom caps with olive oil cooking spray on both sides.
4. Then you sprinkle with 1/8 teaspoon pepper, ¼ teaspoon kosher salt, and ¼ teaspoon garlic powder.
5. At this point, you broil 5 minutes on each side, or until just tender.
6. This is when you remove mushrooms from oven; drain any liquids.
7. Furthermore, you switch oven from broil to bake, setting temperature to 400 degrees F.
8. After that, you break an egg into each mushroom.
9. Sprinkle with the cheese; bake for about 15 minutes, until egg whites are cooked.
10. In addition, you sprinkle the eggs with the remaining ¼ teaspoon salt and 1/8 teaspoon pepper.
11. Finally, you garnish with parsley, and serve.

## Notes

1. Remember that stuffed and baked Portobello mushrooms can become soggy.
2. In order to avoid sogginess:
3. First, make sure you wipe clean, don't wash them (they absorb water).
4. Secondly, pre-broil to release some of the water.
5. Then in the final stage of baking, bake just until the egg whites are cooked.

**NOTE:** baking too long will result in mushy mushrooms that have released their liquid into the eggs. even if that happens, I suggest you carefully drain the liquid, and place the mushrooms on paper towels to soak as much of the liquid as you can.

The Husband Protein Smoothie

# Total Time: 4 mins.

## Yield: 1

## Ingredients

> 1 cup of frozen strawberries
>
> 2 tablespoons of maple syrup
>
> 1-2 tablespoons of almond butter
>
> ¼ cup of rolled oats
>
> 1 cup of frozen wild blueberries
>
> 2 cups of baby spinach
>
> 1 ¼ cups of water
>
> 3 tablespoons of hulled hemp seeds
>
> 1-inch fresh ginger (peeled and roughly chopped)

## Directions:

1. First, you place all ingredients into the blender and blend until super smooth.
2. Enjoy!

Tofu Scramble with Roasted Tomatoes Recipe

**Serves 4**

**Prep time: 10 minutes**

**Cook time: 30 minutes**

**Ingredients**

2 tablespoons of olive oil (divided)

1 tablespoon of brown sugar

¼ teaspoon of freshly ground black pepper

2 teaspoons of dried mixed herbs (preferably an Italian blend)

2 (about 14-ounce) packages extra-firm tofu, drained

2 zucchini (diced)

½ cup of nutritional yeast

4 tomatoes

1 tablespoon of red wine vinegar

¼ teaspoon of kosher salt

2 teaspoons of garlic powder

2 teaspoons of ground turmeric

1 yellow onion (diced)

1 red bell pepper (diced)

8 ounces' button mushrooms (sliced)

**Directions:**

1.  Meanwhile, you heat oven to 400° F.

2. After which you quarter each tomato and cut each quarter in half crosswise.
3. After that, in a medium bowl, toss together tomatoes, vinegar, 1 tablespoon olive oil, sugar, salt and pepper. Transfer to a baking sheet and bake until soft and slightly caramelized, 25-30 minutes.
4. Then, in a medium mixing bowl, combine garlic powder, dried herbs and turmeric.
5. At this point, you crumble the tofu in the bowl and mix to combine; set aside.
6. This is when, you heat a large skillet over medium heat.
7. Furthermore, you add remaining 1 tablespoon oil and sauté the onion about 4 minutes until it's soft and translucent.
8. After that, you add zucchini, bell pepper and mushrooms; cook about 5 minutes until tender.
9. Finally, you add tofu and nutritional yeast and cook, stirring often, until heated through, about 4 minutes.
10. You can serve with roasted tomatoes.

Peanut Butter Cup Protein Overnight Oats

## Yields: 1 serving

Tips: This healthy breakfast recipe is full of rich chocolate and sweet peanut butter flavors. The recipe tastes like peanut butter cup candies and is easily doubled, tripled, or even quadrupled to serve more, and the oats will last for at least 4 days if stored in an airtight container in the refrigerator.

### Ingredients:

½ cup (about 120g) plain nonfat Greek yogurt

1 tablespoon (about 7g) peanut flour (I prefer Protein Plus)

16 drops vanilla crème stevia (or to taste)

¼ cup (about 25g) old-fashioned oats (gluten-free if necessary)

¼ cup (about 60mL) nonfat milk

1 tablespoon (about 5g) unsweetened cocoa powder

## Direction:

1. First, you add all of the ingredients to a glass jar or plastic container with a tight-fitting lid, and stir until thoroughly combined.
2. Then you cover and refrigerate overnight, or at least 8 hours, before eating.

**Notes:** Overnight oats are meant to be eaten cold, straight from the refrigerator! You don't need to heat them up.

3. However, instant oats (aka: quick-cooking or one-minute oats) may be substituted for the old-fashioned oats. Remember, do not substitute steel-cut oats; they do not soften enough.
4. Finally, to keep the oats clean eating friendly, the only ingredients in the peanut flour should be peanuts and salt (optional).
5. Feel free to substituted any sweetener for the stevia.

Savory Pesto Quinoa Breakfast Bowls

**Total Time 10 minutes**

**Servings 2 servings**

**Ingredients**

**for the breakfast bowls:**

>  2 cups of cooked quinoa

> ¼ cup of homemade pesto

> 1 tablespoon of chia seeds

>  2 large eggs

> ½ an avocado

> 2 tablespoons of hemp seeds

**Ingredients for the pesto:**

> 1 cup of fresh kale leaves

> ¼ cup of pine nuts

> 3 - 4 tablespoons of olive oil

> Salt + pepper (to taste)

>  2 cups of fresh basil leaves

> ¼ cup of nutritional yeast

> 1 large garlic clove

> 1 teaspoon of lemon juice

## Directions:

1. First, you start by adding the eggs to a small saucepan with 1 inch of water in the bottom.
2. After which you bring the water to a boil, cover the pot and reduce to simmer for about 5 - 6 minutes.
3. Then, while the eggs are cooking, add all the pesto ingredients to a food processor.
4. At this point, you process until almost smooth (no large chunks wanted here!).
5. Furthermore, when eggs are done cooking, rinse them under cold water to stop the cooking process.
6. After that, you let stand in a bowl of cold water for about 5 minutes.
7. In addition, you prepare your breakfast bowls: add one cup quinoa, ½ of the avocado thinly sliced and half the pesto.
8. Finally, when eggs have cooled, peel them and slice in half.
9. This is when you add to the bowl and sprinkle with half the hemp and chia seeds.
10. You can season with a touch more salt and pepper, or mix it all together.

Better-for-You Eggs

**Serves 4**

**Prep time: 10 minutes**

**Cook time: 20 minutes**

**Ingredients**

4 ounces' lean turkey bacon

1 tablespoon of flour

4 large eggs, + 2 large egg yolks

2 teaspoons of white vinegar

Fresh ground black pepper and paprika to taste

1-pound of asparagus (trimmed)

2 tablespoons of butter

½ cup of chicken broth

1 tablespoon of fresh lemon juice

2 whole-wheat English muffins (split and toasted)

**Directions:**

1. Meanwhile, you heat the oven to 150° F.
2. After which you fill a large, deep skillet with 1 inch of salted water and bring to a boil.
3. After that, you add the asparagus and cook until crisp-tender, about 3 to 4 minutes; drain and set aside.

4. Then, in the same skillet, cook the turkey bacon about 3 minutes until slightly browned on both sides.
5. At this point, you transfer the muffin halves, bacon and asparagus to a baking sheet and place in the oven to keep warm.
6. Furthermore, in a small saucepan, melt the butter over medium heat.
7. After which you whisk in the flour and cook, stirring, for 1 minute; slowly whisk in the chicken broth and bring to a boil.
8. This is when you cook, whisking, for 1 minute.
9. bring out from the heat, then whisk in the egg yolks, one at a time; stir in the lemon juice and set aside.
10. In addition, you fill a medium to large saucepan with 1 ½ inches of water add vinegar.
11. After that, you bring to a boil then reduce heat to medium-low (water should maintain a few small bubbles).
12. Then you crack one egg into a small dish and partially submerge the dish in the pan and tip the egg into the water.
13. However, repeat with each egg and poach for about 2 minutes until the whites are opaque but yolks are still runny.
14. Finally, you remove each egg with a slotted spoon to a paper towel-lined plate.

## Directions on how to assemble:

1. First, you place an English muffin half on each of the 4 plates.
2. After which you divide the bacon among the muffins and top each with a poached egg and some hollandaise sauce.
3. Then you season with pepper and paprika.

## Smoked Salmon and Cream Cheese Wraps

**Total Time 10 mins**

**Servings: 1**

**Ingredients**

2 oz. of smoked salmon

1¼ oz. of red onion

Pinch of pepper

1 8-inch low carb flour tortilla

2 teaspoons of low fat cream cheese

Handful arugula

½ teaspoon of fresh or dried basil

Directions:

1. First, warm the tortilla in the oven or microwave (NOTE: Warm it between 2 pieces of moist paper towel to keep it from drying out).
2. After which you mix basil, cream cheese, and pepper, and spread it onto the tortilla.
3. After which you top it off with the arugula, salmon, and finely sliced onion.
4. Then you roll up the wrap and enjoy!

Turkish Style Savory Breakfast Bowls {Grain Free, Low Carb}

## Ingredients

14 oz. of gluten free spicy ground sausage or meat (chicken, Turkey, beef, or chorizo)

½ cup of chopped dried Turkish apricots

1 tablespoon of cream (milk or coconut)

½ teaspoon of smoked paprika or hot paprika

¼ teaspoon of ground black pepper and sea salt (each)

1 teaspoon of red chili flakes

6oz goats milk yogurt (plain)

14 oz. diced canned tomatoes (drained)

2-3 tablespoons of chopped green chilies (canned or better still diced)

2-3 tablespoons of chopped fresh parsley (and some for garnish)

1 teaspoon of minced garlic

dash of onion salt

dash of lemon juice

2 hardboiled eggs

## Optional: bacon crumbles

## Directions:

1. Drain tomatoes and green chilies if you are using canned (NOTE: If you are using fresh, be sure to chop extra fine).

2.  After which you place ground chorizo/sausage, tomatoes, and chilies in a skillet on medium heat for few minutes until mixed together.
3.  After that, you add in cream, rest of your spices, diced apricots, and parsley (make sure you save some for topping too).
4.  Then you cook for 10 minutes or until meat is thoroughly cooked through.
5.  At this point, you add a 1 teaspoon or more of lemon juice (to enhance spices) and mix again.
6.  This is when you remove from heat.
7.  Furthermore, you place 1 cup of tomato/meat mixture into individual bowls.
8.  After which you top with ½ a hardboiled egg and 3 – 4tablespoons of goat's milk yogurt.
9.  In addition, you garnish with extra bacon crumbles, parsley, pepper/salt, and red pepper.
10.  Finally, you serve with grain free flat bread and cucumber if desired.

## Notes

You can make this dish vegetarian by using tempeh or scrambled tofu with the tomatoes.

**Tip:**

This recipe is filled with spinach, cheddar, and egg whites for a tasty filling healthy breakfast!

**Total Time 29 minutes**

**Servings 1 quesadilla**

**Ingredients**

½ cup of spinach

1- ounce cheddar shredded (or better still sliced)

sprinkle garlic salt

sprinkle black pepper

Cooking spray

¾ cup of liquid egg whites

1 to rtilla for GF (I prefer Trader Joe's Brown Rice)

Sprinkle onion powder

**Directions:**

1. First, you place a medium size non-stick pan over medium-high heat.
2. After which you spray the pan with cooking spray (I use avocado oil) and add ½ cup fresh spinach to the pan.
3. After that, you sauté the spinach until it is wilted.
4. Then, once the spinach is wilted, then pour the liquid egg whites over the spinach, sprinkle with garlic salt, onion powder, and black pepper. (**NOTE:** DO NOT STIR EGGS; I found it easier to make the eggs, omelet style).
5. Furthermore, once they are almost set, fold one side over the other and continue cooking until they are fully set. (NOTE: you

can flip them if one side starts to brown too much before they are done the cooking.  However, if you break them, it's okay, just try to keep them in as big of pieces as possible, this makes them easier to eat in the quesadilla).

6. At this point, while the eggs are cooking prepare the tortilla; line tortilla with shredded or sliced cheese.
7. In addition, when the eggs are fully set, transfer to the tortilla and fold the tortilla in half to cover the eggs.
8. After which you spray the pan again and place the quesadilla on the pan until both sides are browned and cheese is melted (NOTE: You will need to flip it to brown both sides!)
9. Finally, once both sides have reached your desired crispiness and meltiness level it's ready!

**NOTE:** Be careful it will be hot, I prefer to serve mine with guac and salsa to cool it down (temperature wise) and because, guac and salsa, duh.

Tofu in Purgatory (Shakshuka)

## Total Time25 mins

## Servings: 2: Serves 2 hungry people

## Ingredients

4 large cloves of garlic

Salt and pepper to taste I prefer 1 teaspoon salt and ½ teaspoon pepper

½ teaspoon of dried chili flakes (NOTE: I suggest you use less if you prefer less heat)

Indian Black Salt (Kala Namak) optional

1 tablespoon of olive oil (it is optional)

1 796 ml can dice tomatoes

2 teaspoons of dried herbs

1 teaspoon of sugar (**NOTE:** it is optional because it helps to bring out the tomato flavor)

1 block of unpressed medium tofu cut into rounds (**NOTE:** around 350g although this doesn't have to be exact)

## Directions:

1. First, warm the olive oil in a skillet and cook the garlic over medium heat until just starting to turn a little brown. (NOTE: use a drop of water instead of the oil to keep the recipe oil-free).
2. After which you add the salt, chili flakes, tomatoes, pepper, herbs and     optional sugar.
3. After that, you simmer over a medium heat for about 5 minutes then add the tofu rounds.

4. Then you turn down the heat to medium-low and simmer for about 15 minutes until the sauce is thickening up a little and the tofu is soft and heated through.

5. At this point, you sprinkle the tofu with a little Indian Black Salt just before serving if you would like an eggy flavor.

6. Finally, you serve with toast, crusty bread or baguette to mop up the juice!

**Serves 4**

**Prep time: 10 minutes**

**Cook time: 15 minutes**

**Ingredients**

½ yellow onion (chopped)

2 tablespoons of chopped green chilies

Pinch of salt

½ cup of shredded reduced-fat Mexican blend cheese

4 large eggs

½ avocado (peeled and chopped)

1 lime (cut into 4 wedges)

3 teaspoons of olive oil (divided)

1 medium tomato (chopped)

Pinch of cumin

4 (about 6-inch) corn tortillas

½ cup of canned black beans (rinsed and drained)

Fresh cracked black pepper

¼ cup of fresh cilantro leaves

**Directions:**

1. Meanwhile, you heat oven to 250° F.
2. After which you heat a large nonstick skillet over medium-high heat.

3. After that, you add 1 teaspoon olive oil and swirl to coat.
4. Then you add onions and cook about 2 minutes until soft and translucent.
5. At this point, you add chilies, tomato, cumin and salt; cook for another 3 minutes.
6. This is when you remove from heat and transfer to a small bowl (make sure you wipe the skillet clean with a paper towel).
7. Furthermore, working with one tortilla at a time, heat over medium-high heat directly on the eye of a burner for about 20 seconds on each side or until crispy with air pockets.
8. After that, you place tortillas on a baking sheet and evenly distribute cheese and beans among them.
9. Then you bake for about 3 minutes until cheese melts; remove from oven.
10. In addition, re-heat the skillet over medium-high heat.
11. Add remaining oil to pan and swirl to coat; crack eggs into pan and cook for about 4 minutes until whites are set.
12. Finally, you place 1 egg in the center of each tortilla, sprinkle with pepper and avocado, top with salsa and cilantro.
13. You can serve with lime.

## Tips:

It is time to wake up to a healthy Spiralized Breakfast Casserole made with wholesome ingredients, bursting with comforting flavors and packed with 20 grams of protein.

## Total Time 50 minutes

## Servings 9 slices

## Ingredients

24 egg whites you can also use 12 whole eggs

½ zucchini spiralized

1 cup of baby spinach

½ teaspoon of basil

salt and pepper (to taste)

1 (8 ounce) package lean ground turkey breakfast sausage I prefer Jenni-O

½ cup of unsweetened almond milk

2 cups of sweet potato peeled and spiralized, about 1 medium sweet potato

1 teaspoon of Italian seasoning

½ teaspoon of garlic powder

## Directions:

1. Meanwhile, you heat oven 350 F.
2. After which you prepare a square 8x8 baking dish by spraying with cooking spray.
3. After that, you bring a medium skillet to medium heat and add the turkey sausage.

4. Then, with a wooden spoon, break down the sausage as it browns **(NOTE:** Once browned, drain the meat then set aside).
5. Furthermore, in a large mixing bowl, whisk together egg whites with salt, milk, pepper and seasonings until frothy.
6. After that, you assemble the casserole by evenly layering the spiralized sweet potato on the bottom of the casserole dish.
7. At this point, you add the meat over the top in an even layer.
8. This is when you layer the spiralized zucchini and spinach on top.
9. In addition, pour the egg white mixture over the top of the casserole.
10. After which you bake in the oven at 350 F 30-37 minutes uncovered.
11. Finally, you remove from the oven and cool 10 minutes in the baking dish before slicing into 9 large portions.

Fried Eggs with Broiled Tomatoes

**Total Time: 10 Mins**

**Yield: Serves 2**

**Ingredients**

> 2 teaspoons of olive oil
>
> 4 large eggs
>
> 1 tablespoon of grated Parmesan
>
> 2 medium tomatoes (halved)
>
> kosher salt and black pepper
>
> 2 scallions (sliced)

**Directions:**

1. First, you heat broiler.
2. After which you place the tomatoes cut-side up on a broiler-proof baking sheet.
3. After that, you drizzle with 1 teaspoon of the oil and sprinkle with 1/8 teaspoon each salt and pepper.
4. Then you broil for 2 to 3 minutes until tender.
5. In the meantime, heat the remaining teaspoon of oil in a large nonstick skillet over medium heat.
6. After that, you crack the eggs into the pan and cook, covered, to the desired doneness, 2 to 4 minutes for slightly runny sunny-side-up eggs.

7. Furthermore, you transfer the eggs to plates and sprinkle with the Parmesan, scallions, and 1/8 teaspoon each salt and pepper.
8. Finally, you serve with the tomatoes.

Eggs with Herbs

# Total Time:10 Mins

## Yield: Serves 4-6

## Ingredients

10 eggs

½ cup of chopped mixed fresh herbs (**NOTE:** such as parsley and tarragon) and scallions (green parts only)

1 ½ tablespoons of unsalted butter

2 tablespoons of milk or better still water

kosher salt and freshly ground black pepper

## Directions:

1. First, you heat butter in a large nonstick skillet over medium heat.
2. In the meantime, in a large bowl, whisk together the milk, eggs, 1 teaspoon kosher salt, and ¼ teaspoon pepper.
3. After which you pour into the pan and cook, stirring occasionally, to desired doneness, for about 4 to 5 minutes.
4. Then you fold in herbs and scallions.

Greek Frittata

**Total Time: 40 Mins**

**Yield: Serves 4**

**Ingredients**

   10 large eggs

   ½ teaspoon of black pepper

   1 pint grape tomatoes (halved)

   8 ounces' feta (crumbled)

   3 tablespoons of olive oil

   2 teaspoons of kosher salt

   1 (5-ounce) bag baby spinach

   4 scallions (preferably white and green parts), thinly sliced

**Directions:**

1. First, you heat oven to 350° F.
2. After which you add the oil to a 2-quart casserole and transfer to oven for 5 minutes.
3. In the meantime, in a bowl, whisk together the salt, eggs, and pepper.
4. After that, you add the tomatoes, spinach, and scallions and combine. Gently stir in the feta.
5. Then you remove casserole from oven.
6. Furthermore, you pour the egg mixture into casserole.
7. Finally, bake for about 25 to 30 minutes until the frittata is browned around the edges and slightly puffed and a knife comes out clean.

Sausage, Pepper, and Cheddar Omelet

## Total Time 10 Mins

## Yield Serves 1

## Ingredients

> 2 ounces of Italian sausage links (casings removed)
>
> 1 teaspoon of unsalted butter
>
> kosher salt and black pepper
>
> 1 tablespoon of olive oil
>
> ¼ red bell pepper (chopped)
>
> 2 large eggs (beaten)
>
> ¼ cup of grated extra-sharp Cheddar (about 1 ounce)

## Directions:

1. First, you heat the oil in a large skillet over medium-high heat.
2. After which you add the sausage, breaking it up with a spoon, and bell pepper and cook for about 5 to 6 minutes until the sausage is browned and cooked through and the peppers are tender.
3. After that, you melt the butter in a nonstick skillet over medium heat.
4. Then you add the eggs and cook, stirring and tilting the pan, for about 3 minutes until just set.
5. Finally, you sprinkle the sausage mixture and the Cheddar on one side of the eggs; fold the other side over the filling and add a pinch of salt and pepper.

**Total Time: 30 Mins**

**Yield: Serves 8**

**Ingredients**

> 1 teaspoon of red-wine vinegar
>
> 2 tablespoons of chopped fresh chives or scallions
>
> ¼ cup of heavy cream
>
> 1 tablespoon of olive oil
>
> 1 ½ cups of chopped tomatoes or better still 1 (28-ounce) can plum tomatoes, drained and chopped
>
> 4 to 6 slices whole-grain bread
>
> ¼ pound of prosciutto or good-quality ham, thinly sliced
>
> 8 eggs

**Directions:**

1. First, you heat oven to 375° F.
2. After which in a medium bowl, combine the vinegar, oil, tomatoes, and 1 tablespoon of the chives.
3. After that, you arrange the bread in a single layer in a 13-by-9-inch ovenproof baking dish.
4. Then you top with the prosciutto and the tomato mixture.
5. At this point, you break the eggs on top and drizzle with the cream.
6. Furthermore, you bake for about 15 to 20 minutes until the whites have set but the yolks are slightly runny.
7. Finally, you sprinkle with the remaining tablespoon of chives.

Scrambled Eggs with Asian Greens

**Total Time: 15 Mins**

**Yield: Serves 4**

**Ingredients**

2 tablespoons of olive oil

1 tablespoon of cold butter

2 tablespoons of grated Parmesan cheese

toasted bread slices (it is optional)

12 large eggs (beaten)

2 scallions (coarsely chopped)

½ cup of cherry tomato halves

2 cups of (1/2 package) mixed Asian salad greens or baby spinach

kosher salt and freshly ground pepper

**Directions:**

1. First, you beat the eggs in a large bowl until well blended.
2. After which you heat the oil in a large, preferably nonstick skillet and sauté the scallions for about 1 minute.
3. After that, you add the eggs and butter and cook, stirring, until the eggs are just cooked but still soft and creamy.
4. Then you remove the eggs from heat and toss with the Parmesan, tomatoes, and greens.
5. Finally, you season to taste with salt and pepper.
6. You can serve with bread (if desired).

Baked Eggs with Cream and Herbs

**Total Time 20 Mins**

**Yield**

**Serves 4**

**Ingredients**

> 8 tablespoons of heavy cream
>
> 1 tablespoon of chopped fresh herbs (such as parsley and dill)
>
> toast, for serving
>
> 1 tablespoon of unsalted butter (softened)
>
> 8 large eggs
>
> kosher salt and black pepper

**Directions:**

1. First, you heat oven to 425° F.
2. after which you coat four 4-ounce ramekins with the butter (NOTE: In each ramekin, place 2 tablespoons cream).
3. After that, crack 2 eggs into each ramekin.
4. Then you season with ½ teaspoon salt and ¼ teaspoon pepper.
5. Finally, bake for 10 to 12 minutes until the whites are set.
6. You can sprinkle with the herbs and serve with toast.

## Your Delectable Setpoint Lunch Recipes

### Tuna White Bean salad

This recipe is packed full of protein and contains tuna, white beans and fresh parsley.

### Prep Time: 15 minutes

### Ingredients

30 oz. of cans cannellini white beans (drained and rinsed)

salt

3 tablespoons of olive oil

2 tablespoons of parsley, chopped (note: you can also use Basil, Oregano or better still other fresh herbs).

14 oz. of tuna (canned in oil)

1 medium red onion (thinly sliced)

ground black pepper

2 tablespoons of red wine vinegar

4 tablespoons of olive oil

### Directions:

1. First, you drain the canned tuna and add to a large bowl.

**NOTE:** if the tuna is packed in olive oil, I suggest you reserve it for use in the dressing.

2. After which you add the white beans to the tuna and stir to combine.
3. After that, you mix the vinegar, oil, and seasonings together.

4. Then you pour over the fish/bean mixture, you may not need to add all of it.
5. Finally, you serve sprinkled with fresh chopped parsley.

Tomato Avocado Burgers

## Ingredients

## Serves 4

1 lb. / 453 gr of grass fed organic ground beef

½ + ¼ teaspoons of fine grain sea salt

1 ripe avocado (divided)

1 tablespoon of mayo (preferably DIY paleo mayo following this recipe)

A handful of alfalfa sprouts

4 large tomatoes

¼ teaspoon of ground black pepper

1 teaspoon of chili powder

2 tablespoons of Greek yogurt

2 teaspoons of fresh lime juice

¼ teaspoon of ground cumin

## Directions:

1. First, you cut the tomatoes in half horizontally.
2. After which with the handle-end of a spoon or a fork, scoop out the seeds and seeds membrane; Set aside.
3. After that, you place half of the avocado in a bowl and mash with a fork until almost smooth.
4. Then you add mayo, yogurt, lime juice and cumin and stir to combine.

5. At this point, you dice remaining half of the avocado and add it alongside ¼ teaspoon salt.
6. This is when you stir gently to combine; set aside.
7. Furthermore, in a bowl season ground beef with black pepper, ½ teaspoon of salt, and chili powder and mix well.
8. After which you divide into equal 4 portions and gently shape each portion into ½-inch thick patty.
9. In the meanwhile, you heat grill (or grill pan) to medium-high heat.
10. After that, you grill patties 3 minutes on each side or until desired degree of doneness.
11. Meanwhile, lightly grease with olive oil a medium non-stick pan/skillet and heat over medium-high heat.
12. In addition, you cook halved tomatoes face down for about 2 to 3 minutes, until they begin to brown.
13. Then you flip and cook for 20 seconds on the other side so that they get a bit of color.

## If you want to assemble burgers:

First, you place a large pinch of sprouts on the bottom part of each tomato, top with a beef patty, about two tablespoons of avocado sauce and finish with the other ½ of each tomato.

## Total Time:15 minutes

This recipe is easy, delicious and takes less than 15 minutes to make – the perfect summer salad bowl!

## Ingredients:

½ teaspoon of reduced sodium Montreal Chicken Seasoning

2 cups of Romaine lettuce (chopped)

1 corn on the cobb with the husk

1 tablespoon of BBQ Sauce (I prefer Harry & David Raspberry Chipotle)

8 oz. of boneless skinless chicken breast

cooking spray

2 small tomatoes (diced)

2 tablespoons of Skinny Ranch Dressing (preferably homemade or store bought)

## Directions:

1. First, you season the chicken with Montreal chicken seasoning (or any seasoned salt).
2. After which you cook chicken on a grill or grill pan sprayed with oil over medium heat for about 5 minutes on each side, or until the chicken is cooked through in the center.
3. After that, you transfer to a cutting board and slice thin.
4. Then you place the corn in the microwave for about 4 minutes (or better still you can peel and boil in water for about 5 minutes).

5. At this point, you peel the husk off the corn, then cut the corn off the cobb.
6. Finally, you divide the tomatoes, lettuce, corn and chicken on two plates, then drizzle with BBQ Sauce and dressing.

## Tips:

This recipe is easy to make low-carb cucumber rolls with turkey, cheese, spinach, pesto, and veggies! It also Fun for kids to put in their own fillings!

## Makes about 18 rolls.

## Ingredients

¼ cup of store-bought basil pesto

6 oz. of deli smoked turkey breast (shredded)

salt and pepper (for seasoning)

3 medium cucumbers (**NOTE:** each will yield about 6 slices)

6 slices of GO Veggie Lactose & Soy Free Mozzarella Slices (NOTE: cut into ½ inch strips)

1 bell pepper (thinly sliced into matchsticks)

½ cup of spinach (shredded)

## Directions:

1. First, you slice the cucumbers lengthwise on a mandolin at about a 2mm setting. **NOTE:** if you don't have a mandolin, I suggest you use a vegetable peeler.
2. After which you place the cucumber slices on parchment paper and pat dry with a paper towel.
3. After that, you spread about 1 teaspoon of pesto on each cucumber, then evenly distribute turkey, cheese, bell pepper and spinach on each.
4. Then you sprinkle with a little salt and black pepper.
5. At this point, you roll up and place seam down. NOTE: if you want an even nicer presentation, I suggest you stick a toothpick in the middle for easy appetizers!

6. Finally, you serve with extra pesto or sauce of choice.

## NOTE:

You can make this recipe a day ahead. All you do is just store in an airtight container in the fridge.

## Tips:

This recipe can be made with or without meat – all with simple pantry ingredients! Minimal prep and awesome taste.

## Ingredients

> 1 cup of uncooked quinoa (rinsed)
>
> 1 (14 ounce) of can refried beans
>
> 1 teaspoon of cumin
>
> 1 teaspoon of onion powder
>
> 6 bell of peppers
>
> 1 (about 14 ounce) can black beans (rinsed and drained)
>
> 1 ½ cups of red enchilada sauce
>
> 1 teaspoon of chili powder
>
> ½ teaspoon of garlic salt
>
> 1 ½ cups of shredded Pepper jack cheese
>
> Toppings! avocado, cilantro, sour cream, etc.

## Directions:

1. First, you cut the tops off of the peppers and scrape out the ribs and seeds.
2. After which in a large bowl, combine the beans, enchilada sauce, quinoa, spices, and 1 cup of the cheese.
3. After that, you fill each pepper with the quinoa mixture.
4. Then you pour ½ cup water into the bottom of a crockpot.
5. At this point, you place the peppers in the crockpot so they're sitting in the water.

6. This is when you cover and cook on low for about 6 hours or high for 3 hours.
7. Furthermore, you remove lid, distribute remaining cheese over the tops of the peppers, and cover again for a few minutes to melt the cheese.
8. Finally, you serve topped with anything you like! Remember, these are also great with chips and guacamole, believe it or not.

## Notes:

1. As for me, my crockpot only fit 4 of the peppers so I had to bake the other 2 in the oven. **NOTE:** I just put some water in the bottom of the pan, covered with foil, and baked for about 45 minutes at 400 degrees.
2. Remember, you can also keep the leftover filling for a day or two in the fridge.

**Serves 4**

**Prep time: 5 minutes**

**Cook time: 12 minutes**

**Ingredients**

2 cloves of garlic (minced)

3 tablespoons of rosemary (finely chopped)

1 pound of lean ground turkey breast

3 tablespoons of parsley (finely chopped)

**Ingredients for Cooking spray**

1 tablespoon of Dijon mustard

1 avocado (sliced)

4 low-carb English muffins

Lettuce leaves

2 tomatoes (sliced)

## Directions:

1. First, you use your hands, mix the garlic, turkey, parsley and rosemary until just combined **(Note:** do not over mix).
2. After which you divide into four equal portions and flatten each into one-inch thick patties.
3. After that, you heat a large nonstick skillet over medium-high heat.
4. Then you coat pan with cooking spray and place patties in pan, in an even layer.

5. At this point, you cook for six minutes, flip and cook for another six minutes.
6. This is when you slice open English muffins and spread mustard on half.
7. Finally, you serve cooked patties in English muffins and top with tomatoes, lettuce, and avocado.

Seared Tuna Nicoise Salad Recipe

**Serves 2**

**Prep time: 25 minutes**

**Cook time: 6 minutes**

## Ingredients

2 cups of petite lettuce leaves

½ cup of cherry tomatoes (halved)

2 mini cucumbers (sliced thin crosswise)

2 hard-boiled eggs (cooled and sliced)

8-ounce tuna steak

Fresh cracked black pepper

1 teaspoon of Dijon mustard

¼ teaspoon of maple syrup

2 teaspoons of capers

2 ounces' French green beans (trimmed)

¼ cup of fresh basil leaves

¼ red onion (thinly sliced)

4 radishes (sliced thin)

Olive oil (cooking spray)

¼ teaspoon of kosher salt

1 tablespoon of fresh lemon juice

1 teaspoon of water

½ garlic clove (minced)

1 tablespoon of extra-virgin olive oil

## Directions:

1. First, you bring a medium pot of water to boil.
2. After which you add beans and cook until bright green and crisp-tender, about 2 minutes.
3. After that, you drain and plunge beans into ice water.
4. Then you drain and set aside.
5. At this point, you arrange basil, onion, radishes, lettuce, tomatoes, cucumbers, eggs and green beans evenly between two plates.
6. This is when you heat a large nonstick skillet over medium-high heat.
7. Furthermore, you coat pan with cooking spray.
8. After that, you sprinkle tuna with salt and pepper.
9. In addition, you add tuna to pan and cook for about 2 minutes on each side until browned on the outside but still pink inside.
10. Finally, you cut thinly across the grain.
11. Make sure you arrange tuna over vegetables.

## Directions on how to prepare dressing:

1. First, you combine lemon juice and the rest of the ingredients in a small jar with a tight fitting lid.
2. Then you shake until well combined and drizzle evenly over salads.

**Yield: 1 cucumber noodle bowl**

**Total Time: 10 minutes**

**Prep Time: 10 minutes**

This recipe is a fun and filling healthy lunch.

**Ingredients:**

> 3-4 Greek turkey meatballs
>
> 1 tablespoon of crumbled reduced-fat feta cheese
>
> red onion, thinly sliced (as little or preferably lot as you want!)
>
> 2 tablespoons of Sabra Classic Tzatziki Dip
>
> ½ English Cucumber (spiralized)
>
> ¼ cup of chickpeas (drained and rinsed)
>
> 1 tablespoon of sliced Kalamata Olives
>
> 4-5 grape tomatoes (halved)

**Directions:**

1. First, in a bowl, pile cucumber noodles.
2. After which on top, add chickpeas, olives, meatballs, feta, onion, and tomatoes.
3. Finally, you top with Sabra Classic Tzatziki Dip and enjoy immediately.

**Serves 4**

**Prep time: 15 minutes**

**Cook time: 7 minutes**

**Ingredients**

1 cup of fresh breadcrumbs (preferably a roughly 2-ounce piece of bread)

¾ teaspoon of chili powder

1 (about 15 ounce) can black beans, rinsed and drained

½ yellow onion (chopped)

2 tablespoons of olive oil

¼ cup of rolled oats

¼ teaspoon of lime zest

¼ teaspoon of salt

1 garlic clove (crushed)

1 egg (lightly beaten)

1 teaspoon of chopped fresh oregano

**Directions:**

1. First, you pulse the oats in a food processor until fine.
2. After which you transfer into a large bowl with zest, breadcrumbs, chili powder and salt.
3. After that, you whisk together ingredients.
4. Then you combine garlic, beans and onions in the food processor and pulse until mixture becomes a thick paste.
5. At this point, you scrape bean mixture into the oat and breadcrumb bowl and mix with a spatula.

6. This is when you add the egg and oregano and stir until just combined.
7. Furthermore, with moistened hands, divide the bean mixture into 4 equal portions and shape each into a 3-inch patty.
8. After which you heat oil in a large nonstick skillet over medium heat.
9. In addition, you add patties to pan and cook for about 4 minutes until bottom edges are browned.
10. Finally, you carefully turn patties over and cook 3 minutes longer or until bottom edges are browned.

**Serves 4**

**Prep time: 30 minutes**

**Cook time: 30 minutes**

**Ingredients**

1 teaspoon of garlic powder

1 ½ teaspoons of sea salt (divided)

1 teaspoon + 1 tablespoon olive oil (divided)

1 bunch of spinach, ends trimmed and leaves coarsely chopped

1 red bell pepper (chopped)

1 pound of lean sirloin steak

½ teaspoon of cayenne

1 cup of quinoa (rinsed)

1 tablespoon of fresh lemon juice

One yellow squash (quartered and sliced into thin ribbons with a vegetable peeler)

## Directions:

1. First, you season steak with cayenne, garlic powder, and 1 teaspoon salt.
2. After which you let sit for about 30 minutes until it comes to room temperature.
3. Meanwhile, you place quinoa in a medium pot with 2 cups of water.
4. After that, you bring to a boil then reduce heat to low and simmer uncovered for about 12-15 minutes until quinoa is tender and has absorbed all the liquid.

5. Then you heat a cast iron skillet over high heat and add 1 teaspoon of the oil.
6. At this point, you add the steak and sear for about 4 minutes per side.
7. This is when you let rest on a cutting board for about 5 minutes before slicing it into thin strips against the grain.
8. Furthermore, you whisk the lemon juice, remaining 1 tablespoon oil and remaining ½ teaspoon salt together in a large bowl.
9. After which you add squash, spinach, bell pepper and quinoa; toss to combine.
10. Finally, you divide the salad and steak among 4 plates.

### Tips:

1. Feel free to substitute chicken breasts for chicken thighs.
2. Remember, each medium sized chicken thigh makes one wrap, double or triple the recipe as needed.
3. As for the spices, if you don't have one or more of a spice it's cool, just be sure to use lots of black pepper.

### Total Time 15 minutes

### Servings 2

### Ingredients

½ teaspoon of cumin

½ teaspoon of garlic or better still onion powder

1 teaspoon of salt

2 tablespoons of hummus

2 chicken thighs (or better still 1 chicken breast)

½ teaspoon of paprika (or better still chili powder)

1 teaspoon of black pepper

1 teaspoon of oil canola, vegetable, corn, or olive oil

2 medium flour tortilla wraps


### Toppings

1 small tomatoes (sliced)

1 tablespoon of feta cheese (optional)

Romaine lettuce chopped into big pieces

¼ small red onion (sliced)

## Directions:

### <u>How to cook chicken:</u>

1. First, you heat grill or heavy duty pan to high heat.
2. After which you pour oil into pan or brush grill with a coat of oil.
3. After that, you season meat with the spices and place on grill or pan.
4. Then you cook for about 3-5 minutes on each side, if you are using thighs cook for 5-7 minutes on each side.
5. Finally, you remove chicken from heat and allow to cool for 5 minutes then shred or cut into big chunks.

### <u>Directions on how to assemble:</u>

1. First, while the chicken is cooking go ahead and prepare the toppings.
2. After which you cut veggies, spread a thick layer of hummus (about 1 tablespoon) on tortilla or pita bread, then top with chicken and veggies.
3. After that, you wrap tightly then wrap again in aluminum foil if desired.
4. Then you serve with a small bowl of hummus or your favorite dip.
5. Enjoy!

## Your Delectable Setpoint Dinner Recipes

### Stir-Fry Sesame Chicken

**Yields: 6 servings**

**Serving Size: 1 cup**

**Ingredients**

2 teaspoons of sesame oil

1/3 cup of clean-eating teriyaki sauce, divided, homemade or store-bought

1 red bell pepper, seeded, stemmed, and sliced into strips

2 cloves garlic (minced)

1/8 cup of sesame seeds

1 tablespoon of canola (or better still coconut oil)

¼ cup of chicken stock

One pound boneless, skinless chicken thighs or breasts, sliced into strips

one yellow or better still orange bell pepper, stemmed, seeded, and sliced into strips

2 cups of stemmed and chopped fresh green beans

½ cup of chopped scallions (sliced diagonally) OR chopped cilantro

**Directions:**

1. First, you toast sesame seeds in a dry skillet over medium heat, stirring frequently; set aside.

2. After which you coat chicken strips in half the teriyaki sauce.
3. After that, you add oil to a pan or wok over medium heat.
4. Then you cook for about 4-5 minutes per side until golden and cooked through; set aside.
5. At this point, you add green beans and water or chicken stock to the pan.
6. This is when you cover and cook for about 5 minutes, until beans are crisp-tender.
7. Furthermore, you add sesame oil and peppers to the pan with the beans.
8. After which you cook uncovered for about 4 minutes.
9. In addition, you add garlic and remaining teriyaki sauce, cook for an additional 30 seconds.
10. After that, you return chicken to pan and add remaining teriyaki sauce.
11. Then you cook for one minute, until warmed.
12. Finally, you remove from heat and sprinkle with toasted sesame seeds; garnish with scallions or cilantro.
13. You can serve with brown rice or noodles.
14. Enjoy!

**Yields: 6 servings**

**Serving Size: 1 cup**

**Ingredients**

1 tablespoon of extra-virgin olive oil (divided)

¼ teaspoon of black pepper (divided)

¼ cup of chopped white onion

½ cup of dry white wine OR better still ½ cup vegetable broth with 1 tablespoon vinegar

2 tablespoons of flour

Small pinch of nutmeg (if grating from fresh nutmeg kernel, only grate two times)

1.25 pounds of chicken breast filets (about two filets), cut into strips, then halved

¼ teaspoon of kosher or better still sea salt (divided)

1 cup of cleaned and sliced baby bella mushrooms

1 clove garlic (minced)

1 (about 14 ounce) can coconut milk (not lite)

2 tablespoons of pure butter (softened)

6 whole sprigs fresh thyme

## Directions:

1. First, you sprinkle chicken strips with 1/8 teaspoon salt and 1/8 teaspoon pepper.
2. After which you place 2 teaspoons of olive oil in a sauté pan over medium heat.

3. Then, once oil is warm but not smoking, add chicken pieces and cook for about 8 minutes, flipping to get a golden color on all sides and cook through.
4. At this point, you remove chicken from pan and set aside on a plate.
5. This is when you add remaining teaspoon of oil, the thyme, mushrooms, and onions.
6. After that, you allow to cook for about 5 to 8 minutes until onions have softened and liquid has been released and evaporated from the mushrooms.
7. Furthermore, you add garlic and cook for an additional 30 seconds; push mushrooms and onions to side of the pan.
8. After which you add wine or broth into empty space.
9. After that, you scrape any bits in the bottom with a spoon.
10. Then you allow at least half the liquid to evaporate; stir mushrooms and onions back in.
11. This is when you combine flour and softened butter; add coconut milk, flour/butter mix, and nutmeg, stir in pan until flour/butter mix is incorporated.
12. In addition, you return chicken to the pan; add remaining salt and pepper.
13. Cook for about 3 to 5 additional minutes, until heated through and thickened to desired consistency.
14. Finally, you remove thyme branches prior to serving (NOTE: many of the leaves should have fallen into the ragout).
15. Make sure you ragout pairs well with spaghetti squash, brown rice, polenta, soba noodles, or quinoa.

Chicken Breasts with Mushroom Cream Sauce

## Yields: 4 servings

## Ingredients

2 cups of sliced baby bella mushrooms, optional criminal or better still button mushrooms

2 tablespoons of flour

3 tablespoons of olive oil (divided)

1 clove garlic (minced)

¼ teaspoon of black pepper

4 boneless, skinless chicken breasts

½ cup of diced onions

¾ cup of milk

2 tablespoons of chopped fresh thyme leaves

¼ teaspoon of kosher or better still sea salt

## Directions:

1. First, you use a meat tenderizer, pound the chicken breasts to an even thickness.
2. After which you salt and pepper both sites of each chicken breast.
3. After that, you place a sauté pan with one tablespoon of the olive oil over medium heat.
4. Then you make sure the bottom of the whole pan is coated with the olive oil.
5. Add the chicken breasts; cook for 1 minute until golden on the bottom.

6. This is when you turn the breasts over and reduce heat to low.
7. Cover the pan with a tight fitting lid and cook for 10 minutes (make sure you keep to time and do not remove the lid while cooking).
8. After about 10 minutes, remove the pan from the heat, still covered, and allow to sit for a 10 additional minutes.
9. At this point, you make sure there is no pink in the middle of the breasts or that a meat thermometer reads 165 degrees F when inserted in the center.
10. Furthermore, you remove chicken from the pan and set aside, covered to stay warm.
11. After that, you add one tablespoon olive oil and the mushrooms and onions to the pan and increase heat to medium.
12. Then you allow mushrooms and onions to cook for 5 to 8 minutes until the water releases from the mushrooms and evaporates.
13. Whisk in 2 tablespoons of flour and allow to cook for about 1 to 2 minutes, until fragrant; add in the garlic and cook for an additional 30 seconds.
14. In addition, you add a thyme, ¼ cup of milk, salt, and pepper.
15. After which you whisk until thickened.
16. Then you add another ¼ of a cup and whisk until thickened.
17. Repeat until all of the sauce has thickened; place chicken on serving plate.
18. Finally, you pour sauce over the chicken and serve.
19. Enjoy!

Butterflied Lemon Roast Chicken

## Yields: 12 servings

## Ingredients

2 lemons (cut into wedges)

8 cloves garlic, 4 cloves minced, and 4 peeled, but left whole

1 tablespoon of minced rosemary

1 teaspoon of paprika

1 whole 4-pound chicken

2 tablespoons of extra-virgin olive oil

2 whole sprigs rosemary

1 teaspoon of kosher or better still sea salt

½ teaspoon of black pepper

## Directions:

1. First, you set oven rack in middle of oven.
2. Meanwhile, you heat oven to 425 degrees.
3. After which you butterfly chicken by placing chicken breast-side down on clean countertop or cutting board.
4. Then, starting at the bottom, cut along the spine with sharp kitchen scissors on both sides; discard the spine.
5. At this point, you flip the chicken over and lay it open (**NOTE**: the chicken skin should be facing up).
6. This is when you combine garlic, olive oil, minced rosemary, paprika, salt, and pepper to make a rub.

7. Furthermore, you loosen chicken skin a little at a time (**NOTE:** Use hands to spread the rub between meat and skin).
8. After that, you place four whole garlic cloves and four lemon wedges on parchment-lined or nonstick baking sheet.
9. Then you place butterflied chicken, skin-side up, on top of the wedges and cloves.
10. In addition, you add remaining lemon wedges between legs and body.
11. After which you place baking sheet in oven and roast for 50 to 60 minutes, until juices run clear and a meat thermometer inserted between the breast and thigh reads at least 175 degrees F.
12. Finally, you remove skin and cut into pieces to serve.
13. Enjoy!

Grilled Pork Chops with Asparagus and Pesto

## Yields: 4 servings

## Ingredients

- 1 teaspoon of kosher or sea salt (divided)

- 1 bunch asparagus, with woody bottoms removed

- 3 tablespoons of extra-virgin olive oil (divided)

- ¼ cup of basil leaves for garnish (optional)

- 4 (about 1-inch thick each) bone-in pork chops

- 1 teaspoon of black pepper (divided)

- 1 cup of cherry tomatoes

- ¼ cup of clean eating pesto, store bought or preferably homemade

- 4 medium bamboo skewers, soaked for about 20 minutes in warm water, or metal skewers

## Directions:

1. First, you rub pork chops with 2 tablespoons olive oil and sprinkle with ½ teaspoon salt and pepper on both sides.
2. After which you cover and allow to sit at room temperature for 20 minutes.
3. After that, you oil the grate of a grill and set to medium heat.
4. Then you add chops and grill for about 20 minutes, flipping halfway through (**NOTE:** internal temperature taken with a meat thermometer should read 145 to 160 degrees).
5. At this point, you toss the asparagus in ¼ teaspoon salt, ½ tablespoon olive oil, and ¼ teaspoon pepper.

6. This is when you add alongside the pork chops, after the chops have cooked for 15 minutes.
7. Furthermore, you thread cherry tomatoes onto skewers and drizzle with ½ tablespoon oil and sprinkle with ¼ teaspoon of salt and pepper.
8. After which you grill asparagus and tomatoes for about 5 minutes, until asparagus is slightly tender and tomato skins have blackened a bit in places.
9. Then, after removing pork chops from grill, allow to rest 5 minutes before serving.
10. In addition, cover veggies until ready to serve (NOTE: tomatoes may be served on skewers or removed from skewers).
11. Finally, you serve asparagus and tomatoes alongside pork chops and drizzle with pesto.
12. Enjoy!

## Yields: 4 servings

## Ingredients

## Turkey burgers

1 large egg (beaten)

1/3 cup grated or preferably finely chopped onions

1 clove garlic (minced)

½ teaspoon of black pepper

2 teaspoons of canola oil or better still cooking spray to lightly coat the pan or grill

1-pound of lean ground turkey

½ cup of plain whole wheat breadcrumbs or better still whole wheat panko

1/3 cup of parsley (finely chopped)

½ teaspoon of kosher or better still sea salt

1 tablespoon of extra-virgin olive oil

## Cucumber salad

½ cup of chopped chives or better still green onions

¼ teaspoon of kosher or better still sea salt

1 cucumber (diced small)

1 medium-sized ripe tomato (finely diced)

2 tablespoons of freshly squeezed lime or better still lemon juice

## Directions:

1. First, you combine all ingredients for turkey burgers, except olive oil.
2. After which you form into 4 to 5 patties.
3. After that, you sprinkle each patty on both sides with olive oil, using fingers to coat; lightly oil grates of grill.
4. Then you set grill to medium-high heat or place a lightly-oiled skillet or grill pan on the stovetop over medium-high heat.
5. At this point, you add patties to grill or skillet and cover (NOTE: cover if using the grill) and grill for about 5 to 6 minutes on each side, until cooked through.
6. In the meantime, mix together all ingredients for cucumber salad.
7. Finally, you serve room temperature or chill until serving.

Clean Eating Taco Salad Recipe

## Yields: 4 servings

## Serving Size: About 3 1/2 cups

## Ingredients

2 ½ to 3 tablespoons of taco seasoning, homemade or better still store bought

1 cup of grated reduced fat cheddar,

½ cup of salsa or better still enchilada sauce (homemade or store bought)

1-pound of lean ground turkey (optional beef)

2 cups of chopped fresh tomatoes

6 cups of shredded or thinly sliced lettuce

1 cup of guacamole (preferably homemade or store bought)

## Directions:

1. First, you cook meat in a skillet over medium heat until browned, for about 8 minutes, stirring frequently.
2. After which you drain any fat and add taco seasoning, and 1/3 cup water.
3. After that, you cook for an additional 3 to 5 minutes, stirring frequently.
4. Then you arrange 4 plates and top with an even amount of lettuce, guacamole, tomatoes, cheese, and salsa.

**NOTE:** If desired, I suggest you add a dollop of Greek yogurt or sour cream.

Enjoy!

**Yields: 4 servings**

**Serving Size:1 cup**

**Ingredients**

½ teaspoon of sea salt

1 egg

½ teaspoon of fresh ground black pepper

4 large zucchini

2 egg yolks

¼ cup of grated Parmesan cheese

4 slices (nitrate-free) deli ham or better still Canadian bacon, diced (Boar's Head was used in this recipe)

**Directions:**

1. First, you use either a spiral slicer or julienne peeler, cut zucchini into noodles.
2. After which you lay noodles on a paper towel and sprinkle evenly with the salt.
3. After that, you let sit for about 5 minutes; squeeze out as much liquid as you can.
4. Then you whisk egg yolks with egg and cheese until well combined.
5. At this point, you heat a skillet over medium heat and cook bacon until crisp.
6. This is when you add zucchini noodles and stir until warmed through.
7. Furthermore, you reduce heat to low and stir in egg mixture.
8. After which, you turn off heat and stir noodles until eggs are just cooked.

9. Finally, you season with black pepper before serving.
10. Enjoy!

Turkey Taco Lettuce Wraps

## Yields: 6 servings

## Serving Size: 1 lettuce leaf taco

## Ingredients

3 tablespoons of taco seasoning (homemade or better still store bought)

1 cup (about half-pint) of cherry tomatoes, halved

12 whole romaine heat lettuce leaves

1 pound of lean ground turkey

½ teaspoon of kosher or sea salt (NOTE: only if not already in the taco seasoning, like in the homemade version above)

1 avocado (peeled, pitted, and diced)

1 cup of salsa (with no sugar added)

## Directions:

1. First, you add ground turkey to a skillet.
2. After which you cook over medium heat for about 8 minutes until browned.
3. After that, you add 1/3 cup water, taco seasoning, and salt (if not already an ingredient in the seasoning).
4. Then you allow to cook for about 3 minutes more; remove from heat.
5. At this point, you double each lettuce leaf so the top fits into the second and you have 6 doubled leaves altogether.
6. This is when you spoon in meat mixture.

7. Furthermore, you add cherry tomatoes and avocado pieces; top each with salsa.
8. Serve and enjoy!

*Slow Cooker Beef Bourguignon Stew*

## Yields: 8 (1 cup) servings

## Ingredients

One-pound russet (Idaho) potatoes, peeled and chopped into large cubes

2 stalks celery (thickly sliced)

1 whole sprig rosemary

1-pound white button mushrooms (halved)

1 bay leaf

3 tablespoons of white whole wheat flour or better still all-purpose flour

3 cups of pinot noir

½ teaspoon of black pepper

1 ½ pounds of lean beef chuck (cut into bite size cubes)

2 carrots (chopped into ½ inch thick slices)

3 tablespoons of extra virgin olive oil (divided)

1 teaspoon of dry oregano

3 thyme sprigs

2 cloves garlic (minced)

1 cup of low-sodium beef stock

10 pearl onions (halved or better still 1 medium yellow or white onion, diced)

1 teaspoon of kosher or sea salt

## Directions:

1. First, you sprinkle beef cubes with ½ teaspoon salt and ½ teaspoon pepper; dredge in flour to coat.
2. After which you put ½ tablespoon of olive oil in the pan over medium high heat.
3. After that, you add half the beef cubes and brown on all sides, for about 5 minutes. (**NOTE:** It is not necessary to cook the beef all the way through, just sear the outsides).
4. Then you repeat with the second batch; set the beef aside.
5. However, in the same pan that the beef was browned in, add ¼ cup of the wine and scrape the bottom, allowing some of the liquid to evaporate.
6. At this point, you add mushrooms, herbs, pearl onions or diced onion, carrots, celery, and 1 more tablespoons of olive oil and cook for about 5 minutes.
7. This is when you add garlic and cook for an additional 30 seconds.
8. Furthermore, you pour everything from the pan into the slow cooker.
9. After that, you add the rest of the stock, wine, the rest of the salt, the potatoes, the bay leaf, and beef cubes.
10. Finally, you cook on high for about 4- 6 hours or low for 8 hours.
11. Enjoy!

## Yields: 4 servings

## Ingredients

## Salmon

About 1 pound thick wild salmon, without skin, cut into about 12 cubes

## Marinade

2 tablespoons of fresh squeezed lemon juice

1 tablespoon of Dijon mustard

½ teaspoon of kosher or preferably sea salt

4 skewers (**NOTE:** if using bamboo or wood soak in warm water for 20 to 30 minutes)

2 tablespoons of extra virgin olive oil

3 tablespoons of minced fresh rosemary

2 cloves garlic (minced)

½ teaspoon of black pepper

## Directions:

1. First, you whisk together all ingredients for marinade.
2. After which you add salmon and let marinate for about 20 minutes at room temperature.
3. After that, you thread pieces of salmon on skewers.
4. Then you coat grates of a grill or a grill pan or skillet with a light layer of cooking spray; set to high.
5. Finally, once hot, add skewers to grill or pan and cook for 3 minutes or so on each side for about 6 to 8 minutes, until the fish is opaque and flakes easily with a fork, basting with any leftover marinade while cooking.

## Yields: 6 servings

## Ingredients

3 cloves garlic (sliced thin)

¼ cup of fresh squeezed lime juice

¼ teaspoon of black pepper

6 large bamboo or better still metal skewers (NOTE: if bamboo, soak in warm water 30 minutes prior to cooking).

1-pound large raw shrimp (cleaned and deveined)

2 tablespoons of extra-virgin olive oil

¼ teaspoon of kosher or sea salt

¼ teaspoon of paprika

¼ cup of finely chopped cilantro or better still parsley (for serving)

## Dipping Sauce (it is optional)

½ teaspoon of each garlic and onion powder

2 tablespoons each: chopped chives, Italian parsley, and fresh lime juice

½ cup of plain Greek yogurt

¼ teaspoon of each black pepper and sea salt

## Directions:

1. First, you whisk together lime juice, olive oil, garlic, pepper, salt, and paprika for marinade.

2. After which you thread shrimp onto skewers, about 5 to 6 shrimp per skewer; place on a plate.
3. Then you pour marinade over shrimp skewers.

## Directions on how to grill:

1. First, you oil grates of a grill and set to medium heat.
2. Then you add skewers to grill and cook for about 2 minutes per side or until pink and opaque, basting with any extra marinade while cooking.
3. Directions to roast in oven:
4. Meanwhile, you heat oven to 450 degrees.
5. After which you lay skewers on baking sheet and roast for about 5 minutes, until pink and opaque.
6. After that, you sprinkle with cilantro or parsley to serve, if desired.
7. Optional Dipping Sauce - Whisk the entire ingredients until combined; refrigerate until ready to use.

## Yields: 4 servings

## Ingredients

2 tablespoon of room temperature pure butter (divided)

1 garlic clove (minced)

½ teaspoon of sea salt

1 tablespoon plus 1 teaspoon curry powder (**NOTE:** use yellow curry for a mild taste or red for bold)

1 can of unsweetened coconut milk

½ cup of freshly chopped cilantro

1-pound of raw shrimp (cleaned and deveined)

½ cup of chopped onions

1 tablespoon of grated fresh ginger

½ teaspoon of black pepper

1 tablespoon of flour

1 teaspoon of coconut palm sugar

1 tablespoon of lime juice (about ½ a lime)

## Directions:

1. First, in a medium skillet over medium heat, add 1 tablespoon butter and shrimp.
2. After which you cook shrimp on both sides until pink, about 2 minutes per side.
3. After that, you place shrimp on a plate and cover with a paper towel.

4. Then, in the same skillet, add onion and cook until tender, about 4 minutes.
5. At this point, you add garlic and cook 1 additional minute.
6. This is when you add salt, ginger, black pepper, and curry powder, stir to combine.
7. Furthermore, you combine 1 tablespoon room temperature butter with flour.
8. After which you add the coconut milk and palm sugar, stir and bring to a boil.
9. Then you reduce heat to a low-boil, add butter combined with flour and cook about 5 minutes until it starts to thicken up.
10. In addition, add the shrimp and cook just about 15 seconds until heated through.
11. Finally, you remove from the heat; add the lime juice and cilantro, stir to combine.

**NOTE:** if desired, serve over a bed of brown rice.

Enjoy!

Savory Lemon White Fish Fillet Recipe

## Yields: 4 servings

## Ingredients

> 3 tablespoons of olive oil (divided)
>
> 2 lemons (one cut in halves, one cut in wedges)
>
> 4 (about 4 to 6 ounces) halibut, cod, or flounder
>
> ¼ teaspoon of kosher or sea salt
>
> ¼ teaspoon of freshly ground black pepper

## Directions:

1. First, you allow the fish to sit in a bowl at room temperature for about 10- 15 minutes.
2. After which you rub one tablespoon olive oil and sprinkle salt and pepper on both sides of each fillet.
3. After that, you place a skillet or sauté pan over medium-heat and add two tablespoons olive oil.
4. Then when the oil is hot and shimmering, but not smoking, after about one minute, add the fish.
5. At this point, you cook for 2 to 3 minutes on each side, so that each side is browned and the fish is cooked through.
6. This is when you squeeze both lemon halves over the fish and remove from the heat.

**NOTE:** if there is any lemon juice left in the pan, pour it over the fish to serve.

7. Finally, you serve with lemon wedges.

**Tip:** I suggest you make this into a meal by tossing baby kale, arugula, or other lettuce greens in olive oil, lemon juice, salt and pepper and having as a side salad.